PANCHATANTRA STORIES

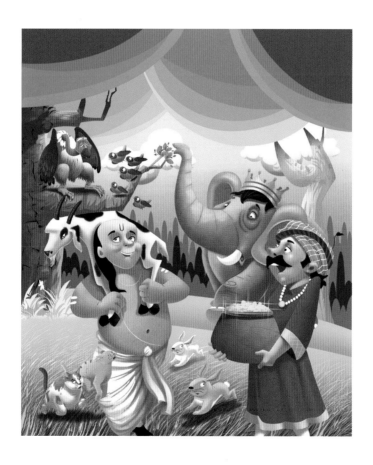

An imprint of Om Books International

Published in 2014 by

An imprint of Om Books International

Corporate & Editorial Office
A 12, Sector 64, Noida 201 301
Uttar Pradesh, India
Phone: +91 120 477 4100
Email: editorial@ombooks.com
Website: www.ombooksinternational.com

Sales Office
4379/4B, Prakash House, Ansari Road
Darya Ganj, New Delhi 110 002, India
Phone: +91 11 2326 3363, 2326 5303
Fax: +91 11 2327 8091
Email: sales@ombooks.com
Website: www.ombooks.com

ISBN : 978-93-82607-89-2

Printed at EIH Press, Gurgaon, India

10 9 8 7 6 5 4 3 2 1

Contents

The Blind Vulture

There was once a tree, which was home to many birds. One day, a blind old vulture came to live in a hole in that tree. The birds welcomed him and gave him a share of their food as he was old. The vulture protected their babies in return. So, they lived happily. One day, a cat passing by that tree heard the baby birds chirping happily.

But, as soon as they saw the cat, they began to cry! The vulture shouted at once, "Who is there?" Now, the clever cat knew that the only way she could eat the tasty tiny birds was if she became good friends with the vulture. She said to him, "I have heard so much about your intelligence from the birds on the banks of the river that I just had to come and meet you, Sir." The vulture felt very good when the cat praised him. He asked, "Who are you?" She said, "I am a cat." The vulture shouted, "Go away otherwise I'll eat you up." The clever cat said, "But I don't eat meat!"

The vulture replied, "How can I trust you?!"

The cat replied, "God punishes those who kill others. I would never kill for food when there are such tasty fruits and herbs to eat in the forest."

The kind vulture believed her and allowed her to stay with him on the tree. Now, the cat would eat one baby bird each day and the blind vulture wouldn't even come to know. Soon the parent birds found out that their children were missing! When they began to look for them, the cat got scared and disappeared into the forest.

When the parent birds came to the vulture to question him, they found him sleeping. And guess what else they found there? A huge pile of bones! The cat would eat the baby birds and leave the bones in the vulture's tree hole.

All the parent birds were very angry at the vulture. They thought he had broken their trust. They attacked the sleeping vulture.

By the time the vulture figured out that the cat had eaten the baby birds, he had already been thrown out and was homeless. His blind faith in the cat had doomed him.

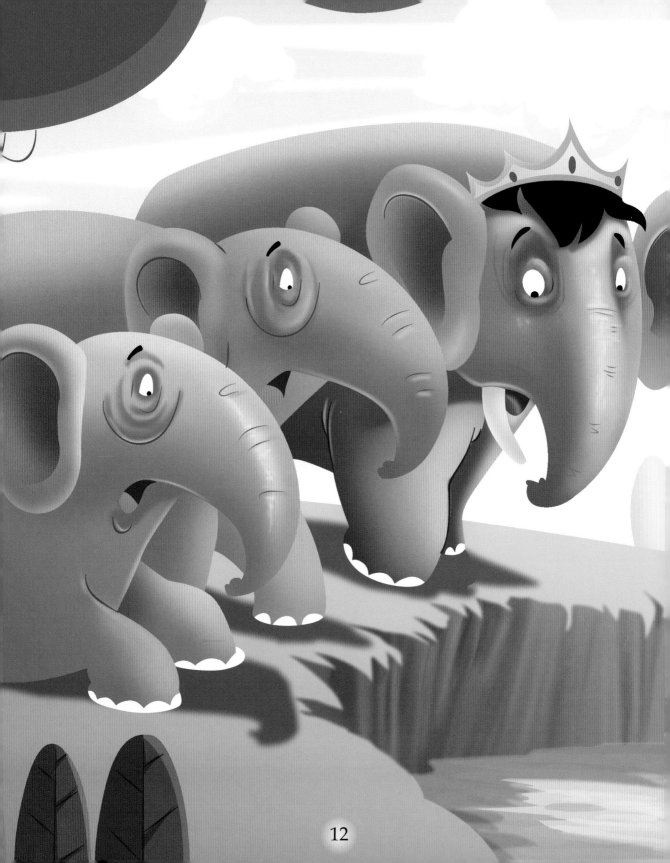

The Clever Hare

A long time ago, the great king of elephants ruled over the forest. Once during his rule, all the lakes became dry as there had been no rainfall for a long time. So, all the elephants came to the king for help and cried that they would all die without water! The elephant king said, "Don't worry! I know about a hidden lake that is always full of water. Let's go there."

While the elephants marched towards the lake, they trampled upon hundreds of hares that had been living there for years. Hundreds of them died and thousands were injured.

The hares were worried. One of them said, "The elephants are so huge and heavy, and we are like ants to them. They will continue to trample us every day while going to the lake for water! If we don't do something quickly we will all be killed."

A smart hare came up with a clever plan and that night he went to the elephant king. He bowed down to the king with great respect and said, "The Moon God has sent me, Your Majesty. This lake belongs to him and he has forbidden all of you from drinking water from it."

"But where is your lord, the Moon?" asked the surprised king.

The hare took the elephant king to the lake, and showing the reflection of the moon in the lake, said, "There he is, the Moon God! Can you see him?"

The elephant king looked down in the lake and replied humbly, "Yes, I can see him." "Salute him and leave. Otherwise, he will be angry and harm you and your subjects," warned the hare. And the elephant king left quietly. The elephants never returned to the lake and the hares lived happily. Despite being weaker, the hare ensured the survival of his race with his cleverness.

The Three Foolish Scholars

In a small town, there once lived four brahmin scholars who were great friends.

One day, one of the scholars told his scholar friends, "If we go to faraway courts of great kings, our wisdom will earn us fame and fortune."

The others agreed, and they all set out on their journey immediately. On the way, they came across the bones of a dead lion.

The first scholar said excitedly, "Let's test the power of our knowledge. Let's try and bring this dead lion back to life! I can put together its skeleton perfectly."

"I can fill the skeleton with flesh and blood," boasted another.

"I can breathe life into its body so that it becomes a living creature," said the third scholar.

The fourth scholar did not boast about his skills.

He simply, shook his head and said, "Very well, please do as you wish, but wait till I climb a tree. You have the power to bring a dead beast to life and soon it will be alive and roar."

"However, I am not sure, if you have the power to change its nature. A lion never eats grass, just as a lamb never eats flesh."

His friends laughed at him. "You are a coward. Shame on you!"

One of them said, "You have no idea that we enjoy complete control over the creatures we create. Why should the lion threaten us when we are the ones to bring it to life?"

Another friend said, "Please feel free to hide anywhere you want and watch us do our magic!"

The fourth friend quickly ran and climbed up a tree. Other scholars got to work.

When the third scholar breathed life into the lion, it stirred and awoke. Then, with a mighty roar, it leapt upon the scholars and ate them up in minutes. The scholar on the tree thanked God for giving him the common sense not to interfere with God and his creations.

The Donkey with No Brains

The lion, the king of the forest, had grown old. Being weak, he could not hunt forhis food. So, he called the fox and said, "I appoint you as my minister. You must advise me on all the affairs of the forest and also bring me an animal to eat every day."

One day when the fox was on a hunt, he met a donkey and said, "You are very lucky. Our king, has chosen you to be his chief minister." The donkey said, "I am afraid of him. He might kill me and eat me up. I don't want to be a minister!"

The cunning fox laughed and said, "Oh, you don't know your great qualities! Our king has chosen you because you are wise, gentle and hardworking. Now, come with me and meet him. He will be really happy to see you."

The stupid donkey was convinced and went along with the fox.

As soon as they entered the lion's cave, it pounced on him and killed him instantly.

As the lion sat down to eat his meal, the fox said, "Your Majesty, I know you are very hungry, but the king must take a bath before his meal."

The lion agreed and said, "You are right. I shall bathe first. Please keep a watch on my meal."

The fox sat down silently to keep a watch on the king's meal. He was very hungry and thought to himself, "I took all the trouble of getting the donkey here so I deserve the best portion of the meal."

Thus, the fox cut open the head of the donkey and ate its brain. When the lion returned found that the head of the donkey had been cut open.

He asked the fox, "What happened to the head of the donkey?"

The fox replied, "Your Majesty, don't you remember that you had given the poor donkey a powerful blow on the head when you killed him?" The lion was satisfied with the answer and sat down to eat his meal.

Suddenly, he shouted, "What happened to the donkey's brain? I wanted to eat it first." The fox smiled and replied, "Your Majesty, donkeys have no brains. If this one had any, he would not have come here to become your meal!" The donkey let flattery overrule its common sense and paid the price.

The Brahmin and the Goat

Once upon a time, a brahmin was carrying a goat on his shoulders and going home. As he was walking on the road, two thieves spotted him. They would plan and coordinate each and every move, together. When they saw the goat with the brahmin, they wanted to steal his goat.

They decided not to rob the brahmin then as it was day time and they were on a very busy street. However, the thieves continued to follow the brahmin, waiting to catch him at a lonely spot. After walking some distance, the brahmin walked through a lonely forest.

The thieves thought that it would be the ideal place to rob the brahmin. They hatched a plan.

Soon, one of the thieves blocked the brahmin's path. The thief said with an expression of shock on his face, "Why are you carrying such a dirty dog on your shoulders?"

The brahmin got angry and said, "Are you blind? Can't you see that I am carrying a goat?" "I don't see a goat, I see a dog," replied the thief.

The brahmin looked at his goat carefully and said, "I am sure that what I have is a goat and not a dog.

I think either you have never seen a goat or you are mad. Whatever you are, let me have my goat and go my way."

The brahmin resumed walking when the second thief came and said, "Good heavens! Why are you carrying a dead calf on your shoulders?"

The brahmin was more confused this time. He lost faith in his own senses.

"What kind of a beast am I carrying?" the brahmin thought in panic. "Perhaps it is a demon that can change its form." He threw the goat off his shoulders and ran away. The thieves quickly grabbed the goat and laughed aloud.

One should use one's own intelligence when judging any situation.

The Tale of the Two Cats

A poor old woman once lived in a hut with a small thin cat. The cat lived on leftovers and gruel that the woman occasionally gave him.

One morning, the cat saw a fat cat sitting on the wall of the neighbour's house.

The thin cat called out to him, "My dear friend, it seems you get to feast at a banquet every day. Pray, tell me where you find so much food?"

The fat cat replied, "At the King's table, of course. Every day, before he sits down to eat, I hide under the table and eat the tasty pieces of food that drop from it."

The thin cat let out a long sigh of longing, and the fat cat said, "I can take you to the king's palace tomorrow. But remember, once we are there, you will be on your own."

"Oh thank you!" purred the thin cat joyfully, and he ran to tell his mistress.

The old woman was unhappy to hear him. "I beg you to stay at home," she said. "What will happen if the royal servants catch you stealing?"

But the thin cat was so greedy that he paid no heed, and the two cats started for the palace excitedly.

Now it had so happened that the day before, cats had entered the King's banquet hall in such large numbers that the angry King had issued an order that any cat entering the palace gates would be put to death instantly. As the fat cat was creeping in through the gate, another cat, who was running away warned him of the King's orders. The fat cat immediately turned and ran away.

But the thin cat was already close to the banquet hall. In a fit of excitement, he leapt to snatch a piece of fish from a serving bowl, when a royal servant grabbed him and killed him. Their is no greater tragedy than being consumed by greed.

The Price of Greed

The King of Benaras had a very clever minister who always gave the King sound advice. Pleased with his service, the King appointed him as the village headman, responsible for collecting taxes.

The villagers greatly respected their headman. They trusted his decisions completely and followed his advice without raising any questions. However, he was greedy and wanted to collect as much wealth as he could. So he made friends with some robbers and struck a wicked deal with them.

"I'll take the villagers to the jungle and when they are away, you can rob their houses. But remember, you will have to give me half of the loot," the headman said.

So a day was decided upon, and the headman led the villagers to the nearby jungle saying they needed to hunt some deer for the village feast. The trustful villagers happily accompanied him, singing merrily on the way.

Meanwhile, the robbers entered the village, robbed all the valuables and took away the cattle. On the same day, a merchant from a distant land happened to come to trade in that village. When he saw the empty houses, he decided to wait on the outskirts till the villagers returned.

As he waited he caught sight of the robbers running away with the loot. He also saw that the headman was leading the villagers back to the village, asking them to beat their drums loud so as to chase away any wild animals close by. But it was just another of his tricks to warn the robbers of the villagers.

When the villagers reached the village, they were shocked to see that all their belongings had gone. "What will we do now? We are ruined," they cried.

Pretending to be very sad and concerned, the headman said, "This is indeed a serious wrong done to us. We have to find the thieves and punish them."

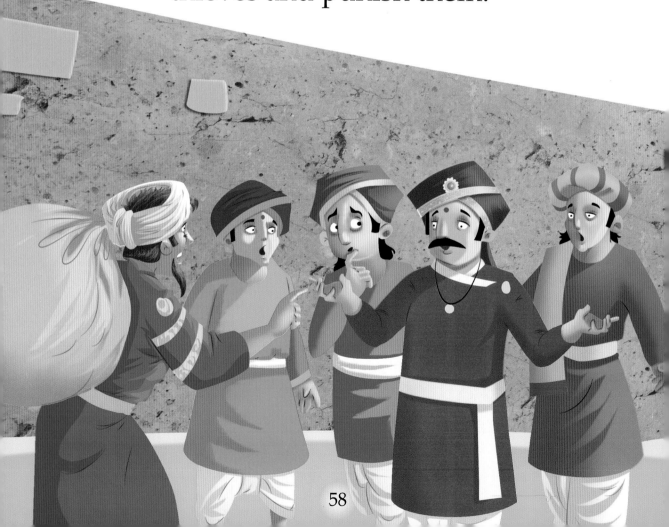

Just then the merchant walked up to the villagers and said, "This headman is a cheat. He's the one who helped the thieves run away with your valuables by asking you to beat the drums while returning from the jungle." The angry villagers reported the matter to the king. On investigating, the headman was found guilty.

The king told the headman, "You will not only be punished strictly, but your honoured title, privileges and luxuries will be taken away. Your greed has cost you a lot."

With this, he sentenced the greedy headman to life imprisonment and gave each villager a hundred gold coins and a cow as compensation for their loss.

The Wise Weaver

Somilaka was an expert weaver who could make the finest garments fit for kings and princes. But he was very poor, and so he decided to try his luck at another place called Vardhamanapuram. Working day and night, he managed to earn 300 gold coins within three years. He decided to return home now.

On his way back, he found himself in the middle of a forest. He climbed a tall tree and went to sleep on a high branch. He dreamt about the God of Action and the God of Destiny talking to each other.

The God of Destiny asked the God of
Action, "This weaver is not destined to
live in luxury. Why did you give him
300 coins?"

The latter replied, "I have to give what
they deserve to those who work hard.
Whether the weaver can keep it or not
is in your hands."

The dream jolted the weaver awake. He looked into his bag and found his coins missing. Heart-broken, Somilaka began crying, "I cannot go home and face my wife a penniless man." He decided to go to Vardhamanapuram and try to earn money again.

This time, he made 500 gold coins in one year. This time too he had the same dream, and found himself penniless when he woke up.

Somilaka lost all hope and decided to kill himself. Suddenly he heard a voice in the skies: "O Somilaka! I am Destiny, the one who took away your wealth. But I am pleased with your hard work and sincerity. Make a wish, and I shall grant it."

"Please give me lots of wealth," asked the weaver.

"In that case, go back to Vardhamanapuram where you will find two wealthy merchants, Guptadhana and Upabhuktadhana. Study them well and decide if you want to be like Guptadhana, the man who earns a lot but does not spend his wealth, or Upabhuktadhana, the man who earns less but also enjoys his wealth."

Somilaka immediately left
for Vardhamanapuram.

He went to Guptadhana's house
and requested him to stay for the night.
Guptadhana agreed and grudgingly gave
dinner to Somilaka.

Later, Somilaka visited Upabhuktadhana's house. Here he was welcomed with great love and respect. The weaver had a good meal and slept soundly. The next day, a messenger from the royal palace came to Upabhuktadhana and gave him a big sum of money for his services provided to the King.

Somilaka thought to himself, "It is better to be like Upabhuktadhana. He enjoys life with whatever he has. What's the use of being rich but miserly?"

Pleased with his choice, the gods showered wealth on him and he lived happily ever after.

A Tale of Two Friends

In a city, there lived two friends named Dharmabuddhi and Paapbuddhi.

Cunning Paapbuddhi planned to rob Dharmabuddhi of all his wealth. He told Dharmabuddhi, "Dear friend, I strongly feel that it is not safe to keep all our wealth at home. We should bury our money in some secret place in a forest. Whenever we need money, we can go there and get it."

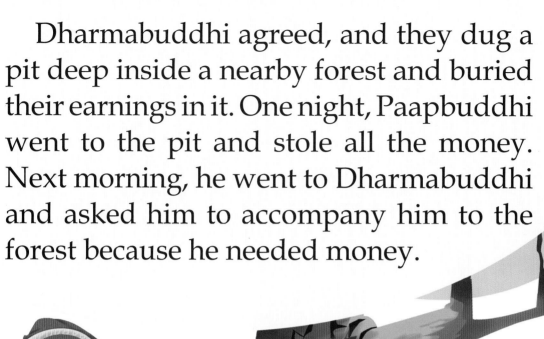

Dharmabuddhi agreed, and they dug a pit deep inside a nearby forest and buried their earnings in it. One night, Paapbuddhi went to the pit and stole all the money. Next morning, he went to Dharmabuddhi and asked him to accompany him to the forest because he needed money.

When both of them arrived at the pit and found it empty, Paapbuddhi began shouting loudly, "Dharmabuddhi, you stole the money. You must give me half of what was buried here." Though Dharmabuddhi insisted that he was innocent, Paapbuddhi continued with his accusations.

The case was brought to the court. Paapbuddhi said to the Judge, "I can produce the gods of the forest as witnesses. They will determine who is guilty." The Judge agreed and asked both parties to be present at the forest next morning.

Paapbuddhi went home and told his father, "Father, I have stolen Dharmabuddhi's money.

There is a court case going on, and I can win it only with your help. Go now and hide in the hollow of the big tree in the forest. Tomorrow morning, when the Judge and others assemble there, I will ask you for the truth. Then you say that Dharmabuddhi is the thief."

The father hesitantly agreed as he loved his son.

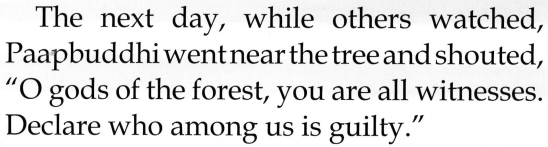

The next day, while others watched, Paapbuddhi went near the tree and shouted, "O gods of the forest, you are all witnesses. Declare who among us is guilty."

The father shouted back from inside the hollow of the tree, "It is Dharmabuddhi who stole the money."

Dharmabuddhi felt suspicious. He filled the tree-hollow with hay, poured oil into it and threw in a matchstick. The fire forced the father to come out of the tree.

"All this is the work of Paapbuddhi's evil mind," the father confided to the judge. The king's men finally arrested Paapbuddhi .

No good come out of being greedy and lying to others. It only paves the path for your fall.

Titles in this Series

ISBN: 978-93-82607-88-5

ISBN: 978-93-82607-76-2

ISBN: 978-93-82607-89-2

ISBN: 978-93-82607-26-7

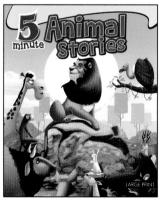

ISBN: 978-93-82607-87-8

ISBN: 978-93-81607-46-6